How to

STOP

Thumbsucking
and other oral habits

MSL
Marshalla Speech and Language

Originally published as *Thumbsucking,* © *1997;* and *How to Help Children Stop Thumbsucking,* © 2000

© 2004, 2001 by Pamela Marshalla. All rights reserved
Printed in United States

Marshalla Speech and Language
11417 - 124th Avenue Northeast
Kirkland, WA 98033
www.pammarshalla.com

ISBN 0-9707060-5-7

Dedication

This book is dedicated to my parents, Alan and Darlene Rosenwinkel. Thank you, Mom and Dad, for raising me with love and guidance, for seeing that I could go to college to become a professional, for encouraging me to succeed, and for standing by me every time things got tough. I love you both with all my heart.

Special Thanks

To Joe Zimmerman and Charlotte Boshart for their contributions to the original edition of this book.

Contents

Introduction

Do you have a child who sucks the thumb? If so, you probably have some of these questions that you hope to have answered:

- Why is it important for a child to stop sucking the thumb?
- Does it damage a child to make him stop thumbsucking?
- How do we help a child stop thumbsucking?
- When do we begin this process?

Thumbsucking is known in professional circles as an *oral habit*, an acquired behavior pattern involving the mouth. It may not be a common subject, but if you're a parent, educator, physician, dental practitioner, or therapist, thumbsucking may become a concern as you live or work with children. Although this book focuses on the elimination of thumbsucking, the same information can be applied to many other oral habits:

- Pacifier sucking
- Finger sucking
- Nail biting
- Lip licking
- Cheek chewing
- Hair chewing
- Tongue sucking

For simplicity, the term *thumbsucking* will be used throughout.

This book is about how to help reduce or eliminate thumbsucking. It is not a medical textbook with technical advice, nor is it a simplistic step-by-step procedure manual. Instead, this is a practical book of ideas, techniques, activities, procedures, plans, suggestions, and guidelines that will prove helpful for most children who suck their thumbs. These ideas can be used effectively by parents who want to help their children, or as a resource for professionals in the fields of speech-language pathology, occupational and physical therapy, education, counseling, and medicine.

PLEASE NOTE: For simplicity, male gender pronouns (i.e., *he, him, his*) are used throughout to refer to the child who sucks the thumb.

Chapter 1

Why Stop Sucking the Thumb?

Six Good Reasons

There are at least six good reasons why a child should eliminate a thumbsucking habit:

1. It is unhealthy
2. It may cause a child's teeth to move out of place
3. It may interfere with a child's development of correct swallowing movements
4. It may interfere with a child's development of correct speech
5. It may affect the way a child rests the mouth
6. It may create unwanted impressions about a child and about his parents

Your Child's Health

Every child needs to learn to keep his hands out of his mouth, and the thumbsucking child is no different. The first reason is health! Thumbsucking is not healthy for a child, because it puts a dirty thumb into the mouth.

Children's hands and fingers seem to be dirty all the time with dirt, food, ink, paint, glue, grease, or mucous. And they don't remember to wash after bathroom breaks either. Yuck! Keeping the thumb out of the mouth helps to keep germs, bacteria, hair, staff, parasites, insecticides, detergents, and more out of the child's digestive system.

Your Child's Teeth

Thumbsucking can interfere with the position and alignment of a child's teeth. In order to understand this better, let's review a fundamental principle from the practice of orthodontics: A slight amount of pressure applied to the teeth over a period of time causes the teeth to move and the bones around them to reshape. Specifically, braces are used to reposition teeth. Under the careful guidance of a professional orthodontist, dental alignment and the position of the teeth can improve significantly.

With thumbsucking, the thumb puts a similar pressure on the teeth and the bones around them, which can move the teeth and reshape the bones. However, unlike braces, thumbsucking can move the teeth into undesirable positions. The changes that occur are direct and observable, but they vary depending upon Three Influence Factors:

- Frequency—the *number* of times per day that the child sucks the thumb
- Duration—the *length* of time the child sucks during each occurrence
- Intensity—the *effort* involved in sucking

These three factors—frequency, duration, and intensity—help determine if a child's thumbsucking will interfere with the development and alignment of teeth and bone structures.

You may have known children whose teeth and mouth were not affected by thumbsucking. Habitual thumbsucking does not always move teeth and bone. For example, if a child sucks the thumb only once in a while, for a short period of time, and with little intensity or pressure, there probably will be no major effects. Such a child might suck the thumb for a few minutes at bedtime but, once asleep, might allow the thumb to fall out. This child's thumbsucking habit would be considered weak, mild, and of little concern. Typically, it is outgrown with little or no intervention. If this is the type of thumbsucking your child does, you probably do not need to be concerned.

On the other hand, if a child's thumbsucking habit is more involved because he engages in it often and intensively, it has a greater likelihood of impacting the child's oral structures. Such a child might suck the thumb many times per day—while playing, watching TV, riding in the car, during meals—and for long periods of time, like most of the night. If so, there could be a greater negative effect on teeth and bones.

Whether a child has a mild or a severe thumbsucking habit, the elimination of the problem will be better for the position and alignment of the teeth.

Your Child's Swallowing Development

Thumbsucking can interfere with your child's ability to develop correct swallowing movements. To better understand, let's look at the swallowing process in detail.

Swallowing is the process of moving food from the mouth to the stomach. In the mouth, food is crushed, mixed with saliva, and formed into a mass. Then the mass is pushed from the mouth into the throat by the tongue. The throat muscles move the mass down, toward the stomach. Swallowing movements develop in two stages. The first stage is known as *infantile swallowing* and the second is *mature swallowing*.

- INFANTILE SWALLOWING: Babies suck and spoon feed in a pattern known as the suckle-swallow, or infantile swallowing pattern. In the suckle-swallow, the tongue alternately moves forward and back, first sticking out and then pulling in, back and forth in a pumping motion. When a baby suckle-swallows food on a spoon, the tongue pushes the food out right after it has been spooned in. Parents patiently scrape the food off the front of the mouth and shovel it back in, over and over, until most of it has been consumed. The key to feeding a baby is to continuously scrape and shovel until the baby swallows enough to satisfy his hunger.

- MATURE SWALLOWING: Here, the tongue no longer moves forward and back. Instead, it moves up and down and left and right, staying inside the mouth. The tongue develops a cup-shaped configuration as the tip and sides of the tongue become more developed to cradle the mass of food. When a child reaches this stage, the amount of outside scraping needed during feeding is reduced dramatically because food can stay inside the mouth and is swallowed more skillfully.

During the toddler years, children usually advance easily from the suckle-swallow pattern to the mature swallow pattern. By preschool, most children have a fairly mature swallow pattern. Typically, preschool children can bite, chew, and swallow everything from soup to nuts, and they do so fairly well.

Thumbsucking and Swallowing

In relation to swallowing, thumbsucking can prolong the infantile suckle-swallow pattern, and it can delay or *prevent* the emergence of the mature swallow pattern. This prolonged infantile suckle-swallow pattern has been called the *reverse swallow* and *tongue thrusting*. Ongoing thumbsucking can inhibit the development of the vertical (up-down) and lateral (left-right) tongue movements required in the mature swallow.

Without a mature swallow pattern, children can have difficulty chewing and swallowing certain foods. Subsequently, they may learn to avoid difficult foods or even those perceived as difficult. Thus, they can become picky eaters.

And another problem can arise. If the in-and-out tongue movements of the suckle-swallow persist beyond early childhood, they can apply too much outward pressure on the front teeth.

Your Child's Speech Development

Chronic thumbsucking and other oral habits can interfere with a child's speech development in two ways. First, it can delay the emergence of early speech in young children. Second, thumbsucking can interfere with an older child's ability to learn the later-developing speech sounds, which are more difficult to produce because they require the use of refined tongue movements.

Emerging Speech

Simply put, excessive thumbsucking can interfere with the emergence of speech in young children because a thumb in the mouth usually keeps a child quiet. Thumbs, fingers, pacifiers, or bottles are hampering some toddlers who have not begun to talk. Once the thumb or other object is removed from the mouth and their hands get busy with other things, little children can begin to develop speech like other children their age. Barring other problems, most will catch up with their peers in a short time.

Later Speech

Habitual, long-term, and excessive thumbsucking can interfere with a child's later speech development when children should be learning advanced speech sounds. Speech emerges in most children in a fairly predictable way. For example, the first sounds to emerge are those that are easy to produce. This set includes *m, b, w, d, n, g, y,* and others. Early-developing sounds do not require refined oral movements; therefore, they are easy to learn. Excessive thumbsucking usually will not hamper the correct production of these sounds.

Later-Developing Sounds

SOUND	SAMPLE WORD
S	Soap
Z	Zoo
SH	Shoe
ZH	Television
CH	Church
J or G	Judge
L	Love
R	Run

However, later-developing sounds require refined or advanced tongue movements, particularly:

- Tip elevation
- Lateral tongue elevation

- Midline tongue depression
- Lateral back tongue elevation
- Posterior tongue stability
- Ability to control fine differences in tension in the entire tongue

When thumbsucking is present and a child continues to overuse the infantile suckle-swallow pattern, it can delay or change his ability to move the tongue in these refined ways. The tongue becomes clumsier, with less differentiation of movement in its various parts, like moving in the middle instead of the tip and sides. Advanced sounds can become distorted, are omitted from speech altogether, or they are substituted for other, easier-to-produce sounds.

To remediate the errors, speech and language pathologists enroll children in articulation therapy. But success will be limited if the speech problem is the result of an oral habit, an inappropriate oral movement pattern, and/or an oral structural problem. Eliminating thumbsucking may be the first step in solving erroneous speech sounds.

Your Child's Oral-Rest Position

The oral-rest position is that position the mouth assumes when the child is not engaged in eating, speaking, or other oral movements. When in oral rest, the mouth is quiet, unmoving. Excessive thumbsucking may affect the way a child holds his mouth at rest, which also affects overall facial tone and appearance.

Take a moment to notice your own oral-rest position as you read silently. If it's correct and you have optimum oral structure, you should have similar characteristics as those described in the left-hand column of the chart below.

Oral-Rest Position Characteristics

Normal	Thumbsucking
Lips Rest gently together	**Lips** Not touching; protruded
Teeth Upper and lower don't touch	**Teeth** Positioned too far apart (jaw is low)
Tip of Tongue Rests gently upward against the roof of the mouth, just behind the upper front teeth	**Tip of Tongue** Cannot reach the roof of mouth behind the upper front teeth
Sides of the Tongue Nestle gently against the insides of the top, side, and back teeth	**Sides of the Tongue** Cannot reach the palate
Middle of the tongue Relaxed and low	**Middle of the tongue** Pushed upward or forward

Correct oral rest provides an experience base to help develop optimum lip and tongue muscle movements, as well as jaw position in eating and speaking. A correct oral-rest position cannot be achieved when a thumb or finger is in the mouth.

Try this: Place your thumb in your mouth as if you were going to suck it. Notice how your jaw, lips, and tongue are positioned and how they alter the oral-rest position. These are presented in the right-hand column above.

When a child sucks the thumb often, the muscles of the mouth exercise in this fashion and the teeth and bones reshape to accommodate the thumb. From the front, his mouth begins to look different, even when the thumb is not there: The mouth rests open, the lower lip sags, the upper lip may be taut, and the tongue may be protruding. Professionals describe this as *open-rest posture* or *open-mouth posture*. Such a child may breathe through the mouth instead of his nose, which can cause the lips and mouth to become dry and chapped.

As a strong habit, thumbsucking causes the muscles of the mouth to develop differently. Speech and swallowing difficulties/differences arise, as well as problems in growth and development of the teeth. A chronically lowered jaw can alter the way a child's face grows, resulting in a longer, thinner face.

Your Child's Social Acceptance

Not only can thumbsucking affect your child's health, teeth, swallowing, speech, and facial appearance, but other people may impugn the child who sucks the thumb—or cast aspersions on the child's parents. To some people, a child who sucks the thumb appears different, unusual, immature, shy, insecure, afraid, less intelligent, withdrawn, poorly behaved, stressed, or bored. Or it may appear that the child's parents have no control over him, do not care about him, are unwilling to tend to his needs, are in denial, are less intelligent, or are unwilling to tackle a difficult problem.

Facing these realities is an important part of your decision to help your child eliminate his thumbsucking habit.

Summary

Excessive, long-term, and habitual thumbsucking can have a detrimental effect on six areas of a child's growth and development, including his health, teeth, swallowing, speech, oral rest, and social acceptance. The extent of the effects depends on frequency, duration, and intensity of the thumbsucking habit. Although every child will be motivated in different ways to quit, getting rid of thumbsucking is an excellent plan.

Chapter 2

The Evolution of Thumbsucking

*How It Begins and When
It Should End*

In all probability, your child's thumbsucking behavior began during early childhood. As a result, thumbsucking can be deeply rooted and terribly important to your child.

For most children, there are six timeframes in which oral habits develop:

1. In utero
2. Newborn
3. Infancy
4. Toddler
5. Preschool
6. Elementary schoolchildren

Let's look at each of these timeframes in detail.

Thumbsucking in Utero

Unborn babies begin to put their fingers and thumbs in their mouths between three and six months, the second trimester. They are curled up so nicely in the womb that the hands, which have been fully formed since ten weeks, are easily accessible to the mouth. Babies actually suck on their fingers and thumbs during this time. If you have any concerns that your actions may have caused the thumbsucking habit in your child, rest assured that he probably began while he was still in his mother's womb.

Sucking before birth is normal. This is the period when the tiny muscles of the mouth exercise in preparation for the high demands of nutritive sucking after birth. Hand-to-mouth and finger-to-mouth behavior is natural and expected. One would never consider trying to eliminate thumbsucking while a child is in utero; it is both unnecessary and impossible.

Thumbsucking in Newborns

From birth until about two months of age children learn to bring their hands to their mouths without the support of the embryonic sack. At first, very little actual hand-to-mouth behavior is seen, because newborn babies are quite stiff. After a few days or weeks, however, babies begin to loosen up and relax the tightness in their arms and shoulders. When held in a flexed or cradled position, their hands move nearer to their mouths.

Barring disorder, developmental delay, or disease, full-term newborns can suck on a hand, finger, thumb, breast, bottle, or pacifier. Sucking soothes and nourishes a baby during this period, and, since we all like quiet and content babies, the behavior typically is encouraged. Except for the concern about sharp little fingernails—which can be covered with little mittens—most people think nothing of newborn thumbsucking.

Thumbsucking in Infants

By four to six months, most healthy full-term babies have begun to put their hands, fingers, thumbs, and many other objects into their mouths. In fact, mouthing behavior is one of several activities that dominate a baby's play throughout the first year. Babies seem driven to put things in their mouths, including blankets, diapers, rattles, chew toys, other toys, adult fingers, and by five or six months of age, even their own toes and feet. This is the time to baby-proof your child's immediate environment, because it is guaranteed that anything he can get his hands on will go in the mouth. At first, it's just the stuff nearby. But, as he learns to scoot, crawl, and walk, everything in the whole house is fair game!

Sucking is a baby's greatest love. Mouthing behavior, including thumbsucking, is completely natural during infancy. We should expect and encourage it because mouthing soothes a baby, encourages the eruption of teeth, and it is one of their primary means of exploring and playing. They are learning and having fun by putting fingers, thumbs, toys, pacifiers, bottles, toes, and other objects into their mouths. But those objects should be safe—no sharp or small objects that could be swallowed or choked on—and they should be clean.

Almost every parent permits some means of mouthing and sucking for their infant child. During this period of development, oral behaviors like thumbsucking are welcome and are not viewed as inappropriate or undesirable. Sucking a thumb is calming, comforting, securing, friendly, and familiar. Sucking is the activity around which everything else revolves.

Thumbsucking in Toddlers

As babies turn into toddlers, their world expands tremendously. Mouthing and thumbsucking behaviors begin to subside. Although they still desire to put many things into their mouths, they develop their play skills so that they no longer need to depend upon mouthing as a primary means of entertainment. Between two and three years of age, adults should feel comfortable telling a toddler, "Keep that out of your mouth" or, "Don't put your thumb into your mouth." Toddlers don't need to play with objects in their mouths, so we can begin working confidently to help them eliminate these behaviors.

Some parents think that thumbsucking should be treated differently from general mouthing behavior because, although mouthing is for play, sucking is for soothing, comforting, regrouping, and quieting. Some parents are unwilling to prohibit their toddler from sucking. They feel that thumbsucking will stop when the child is ready, or they simply may be afraid to face the behavior problems that might result from the elimination process.

The toddler years are the best time to begin changing a thumbsucking habit. This is the time when all the child's behaviors are changing radically. Their interests are growing; they are gaining a new sense of self; they can be encouraged to explore new toys, books, or play equipment; and they can be easily distracted from one activity to another. In fact, distraction is probably the best technique available to get a toddler's thumb out of the mouth. Give him something more fun and interesting, and often the thumb will come right out of the toddler's mouth.

Thumbsucking in the Preschool Years

Most children stop sucking and mouthing at a certain point during the preschool years and, most of us expect kindergarten children to be done with it. Therefore, preschool and kindergarten teachers often have specific classroom rules about mouthing behaviors. Posted in the room or not, these rules might include:

- Hands down or quiet hands
- Mouths closed
- Keep hands out of the mouth
- Keep toys out of the mouth
- Only put food in the mouth

Preschool teachers often teach songs or rhymes about keeping the hands still in the lap during circle and story time. Such rules help level the playing field, so that all children who go through the school system behave according to the same set of principles. It is expected that from this time forward, mouthing behavior, including thumbsucking, will disappear, and eventually will not be seen at school.

During the preschool years, thumbsucking can become an important part of the child's life. The thumb can become the child's best friend. Life may be busy, boring, or bothersome, but the thumb is always there, ready and willing to be close, intimate, and, from the child's perspective, to care for the child. Thumbsucking is part of life's everyday routine: expected and scheduled. Without it, the day just isn't right—like a morning without coffee. Thumbsucking is as important to the child as a favorite teddy bear or blanket. So eliminating it can be a serious event for a young child, causing him to miss it terribly.

If your preschooler is becoming strongly attached to thumbsucking, it is probably becoming a strong habit that could be difficult to eliminate. Take a close look at the child's thumbsucking routine and start making decisions about when and how to eliminate it.

Thumbsucking in Elementary School

Between five and seven years of age, mouthing and sucking behaviors have disappeared in most children. Remnant or leftover thumbsucking is considered inappropriate when a child enters this age group and beyond. What starts out as an adorable behavior in a child's infancy usually begins to bother us when a child enters grade school. We don't like it, because we worry about germs and the child's appearance, speech, swallowing, or oral-rest position. Adults often become frustrated while trying to deal with a strong thumbsucking habit. It can seem impossible to break. During this timeframe is when most parents finally decide to do something about thumbsucking.

Thumbsucking in Adulthood

It may be a shock for some readers to learn that thumbsucking can be a secret habit into adulthood. Usually, significant differences in dental alignment, swallowing, speech, and oral-rest position are seen in the adult who habitually sucks the thumb. Some people have gone through years of orthodontic treatment to no avail because the oral habit and swallowing problems perpetuate the dental problems after the braces have been removed. Adults who suck the thumb can quit, but just like quitting the habits of smoking or drinking, it's hard. Eliminating a thumbsucking habit in adulthood takes determination, persistence, and often the support of a professional.

Summary

Oral behaviors, including thumbsucking, are a natural part of the life of babies, toddlers, and preschool children. But the intensive mouthing and sucking behaviors seen in these young children should come to an end sometime in the preschool or early grade-school years. If continued by age seven, thumbsucking that is frequent, intense, and of long duration can be detrimental to the child and viewed as both unwanted and inappropriate.

Chapter 3

Foundational Guidelines

Eleven Principles Underlying the Process of Change

It is an honorable decision to help a child reduce or eliminate a thumbsucking habit. The primary goal is to reduce and eventually to eliminate the habit. But an equally important goal is to maintain a mutually healthy relationship between child and parents, teachers, and therapists.

The following are fundamental guidelines for approaching the thumbsucking issue. Parents are encouraged to:

1. Treat thumbsucking as a behavior
2. Make a firm decision
3. Pick a good time
4. Stick to the decision
5. Work at an appropriate pace
6. Adopt a positive attitude
7. Allow the child to make this decision
8. Face possible causes
9. Talk to someone
10. Look to your religion
11. Be patient

Treat Thumbsucking as a Behavior

First and foremost, it is important to understand that there is nothing wrong with the child who sucks the thumb. He is not bad, he is not trying to hurt you, and he is not stupid. The child simply has an undesirable habit, whether or not he's aware of it. All children have behaviors that adults find undesirable. They can be loud, rude, messy, obnoxious, selfish, mean, unforgiving, and uncaring. Children must be trained to act appropriately at home, at school, and in the rest of society. Part of the training necessary for your child may be learning not to suck the thumb. Because thumbsucking is a habitual behavior, it can be treated like all other behaviors that we want to alter in our child. Just like learning not to wet the bed, not to talk loudly in a restaurant, not to dominate toys, not to forget to do homework on time, and not to talk back to parents, learning not to suck the thumb takes time and energy.

Consider the ways you already work with your child to alter his behavior, and ask yourself these questions: How do I get him to . . .

- Sit still?
- Leave his sister alone?
- Eat his vegetables?
- Clear the table?
- Act politely toward others?

The answers will help you understand that you already have many ways in which you shape your child's behavior. Sometimes just a look will bring the child into line. Sometimes it takes explaining the situation. Sometimes a parent has to get downright stern and administer punishment if the child defies the adult's authority. Sometimes a heart-to-heart talk is needed.

If in exploring the answers to these questions you find that you do not know how to control your child's behavior well, and if you find yourself at a loss as to how to handle him, it is suggested that you take time first to learn some basic behavior management techniques. (See appendix.)

You may find that you need time, perhaps up to one year, to learn how to control your child's general behaviors more effectively before you tackle the thumbsucking issue. If so, go for it! Your life will be significantly improved, and it will make your attempt to eliminate thumbsucking much easier.

Make a Firm Decision

Make a firm decision in your own mind before you begin to introduce these ideas to your child. He will have difficulty learning to stop sucking the thumb if you don't believe he can. Any indecision on your part will be transmitted to the child via your words and actions. So, before you begin, you must be convinced that your child can change with help. Be sure you know in your heart that you are doing the right thing. Have confidence that the behavior can and will change.

Remember, your child probably only has you to fall back on. With doubts, your child will feel your uncertainty and will become uncertain himself, doubting his own ability to change or his desire to do so. Have no doubts yourself and your child will be able to depend on you—and he will make it! Be consistent in your belief and in your approach.

"And," you may ask, "what if I don't believe that he can stop sucking the thumb?" Then you have two choices: Quit the process altogether, or fake it. If you quit, your child's thumbsucking will continue. However, if you put up a good front and begin the process, you probably will succeed. Show a positive face, act like it will work, and it will. Give yourself some time to watch what happens. As the process unfolds, you will come to believe that your child can quit thumbsucking.

Pick a Good Time

Plan the process for a time when it best suits you, your child, and your family. Nothing can destroy a good plan more easily than trying to do it when there are too many competing projects. Watch out for events that will interfere with the process, such as vacations, holidays, or pressing needs. Select a time when your family routine is set and fairly quiet. Don't begin this plan with other new lessons or sports activities. Consider using a time when other family members are away and the house is calmer. Or consider a natural beginning point, such as after a major holiday, birthday, or after the end of the school year.

Stick to Your Decision

Once you make the decision to help your child stop a thumbsucking habit, don't give up. If you get off track, get back on when the time is right. Keep in mind that the plan that starts and stops too many times but never really ends in success will be a drag. It is better to abandon the project altogether for a time than to let it drag on without success. Not every child will achieve success the first time around; it may take several tries to eliminate the oral habit. Don't be afraid to postpone the project for a while if necessary, but don't give up. If the project wanes or fails, reread chapter 1 to refresh your drive. Know in your own mind that you will come back to the plan at a later date, and set a time in your mind or on your calendar to restart. Then make another firm decision and get back to it.

Work at an Appropriate Pace

Pace activities so they fit within the ebb and flow of everyday living. It is not good to work on this program all the time. There should be a natural rhythm of work on this area. Just like playing a piano, regular practice is needed. But a child who practices too much may seriously destroy his interest in the piano. Or too much practice may block the development of other skills, like reading, playing with friends, or riding a bike.

Present your child with opportunities to change his thumbsucking habit in ways that fit into the natural comings and goings of family life. A three-minute talk at night while tucking the child into bed may be the only activity for the day. By incorporating your plans into the stream of everyday living, the child will naturally benefit from these ideas.

Adopt a Positive Attitude

Use positive words that offer direction with genuine love, care, and pride. Your child probably has never heard anyone talk about thumbsucking before, except, perhaps, in negative ways. By taking charge of the child's thumbsucking program, you will become the child's mentor on this topic. What you say and do will become quite important. Understand that anger won't work to change the oral habit. It only makes everyone upset.

- "Stop that!"
- "Are you a baby?"
- "Get your fingers out!"
- "I told you to quit that!"
- "What's the matter with you?"
- "I told you! . . ."
- "Aren't you ever going to stop sucking your thumb?"
- "If you don't stop that, I'll . . ."

Do not scold, demand, nag, belittle, talk snotty, or threaten your child into quitting his thumbsucking habit. Scolding may be somewhat effective for the child who only sucks the thumb on occasion, or for one who has just begun to put the thumb in the mouth. But for the child who has a chronic thumb-sucking habit, angry and threatening statements may do more harm than good, with little positive effect on the behavior, especially if the threats are meaningless. Children who receive regular uncon-structive criticism and frightful demands can end up feeling hateful and resentful toward adults. Angry demands make for angry children who may do noth-ing to change their behavior other than to rebel against adult authority. The child who must deal with angry adults will see no real reason to change.

Talk with the child in ways that are informative, instructive, and constructive. Give your child the information he needs to make good choices. Teach him what to do and how to do it. Talk to him in ways that lift him up in the process. Show genuine con-cern. If appropriate by age and developmental level, hold your child on your lap or cuddle with him. Hold him by the hand and have him look you straight in your loving eyes as you discuss ideas.

Remaining positive throughout the process may not be the easiest part of the program. At times, it will be easier to scold or belittle. If you slip, acknowledge that you have done so to yourself and to the child. Let your feelings go and move on. Get back on track and continue to help your child.

Allow the Child to Make This Decision

Above age three, change will occur only after the child has made the decision to change. We want our children to do all kinds of things: make their beds, wear clean clothes every day, make friends, succeed in school and athletics, and be respectful. Included is your want for your child to stop sucking the thumb. But our desires and their desires are two different things. We may want them in gymnastics classes when they want to sing in a choir. It is one of the great lessons of parenthood: to release children from our desires for them. They have to have the freedom to make some decisions on their own. The decision to eliminate an oral habit is a personal one that arises from within the heart of the child. Still, you might be able to talk them into it. However, over time, information and suggestions can influence our children to do a great many things, including breaking an oral habit.

CHRISTINA

I am reminded of a young girl who had a fingernail-biting habit. She came to the decision to stop biting her fingernails when her older sister began to wear fingernail polish and she wanted to as well. She talked about how her sister's fingernails were quite a bit longer than her own. Her mother took advantage of this opportunity by saying, "That's because she doesn't bite her nails. If you want long nails, you can't bite them."

This was all she needed to be motivated to stop the habit. She asked her mother to buy something to help her stop, "Isn't there some kind of stuff we can put on my nails that will taste icky?" Her mother bought a bad-tasting product designed to eliminate nail biting and thumbsucking, and the child quit with just this little bit of help. The habit resurfaces on occasion, so the mother reminds her that she needs to wear the solution again for a few days. Because she wants to be like her big sister and other girls who have pretty nails, Christina is self-motivated to do it.

JASON

A young boy refused to stop his thumbsucking habit. At his four-year checkups, neither the pediatrician nor the dentist thought it was a problem. Therefore, the boy was convinced it wasn't a problem either. He refused to give it up when his mother began to talk about it.

However, at his five-year checkups, both the dentist and the pediatrician did an about face and told him he'd have to stop because it was unhealthy and it was affecting his teeth. That was it! This literal young boy only had to hear once from these professionals that it was bad and he stopped, almost overnight, with the help of a little bandage on his thumb as a reminder.

We can plan an attack on thumbsucking by looking at what might motivate the child to change, by setting up the environment in ways that encourage change, by saying things that suggest change, and by helping the child change once he makes his decision.

Face Possible Causes

Sometimes there are identifiable factors that contribute to a child's thumbsucking habit. Although a specific thumbsucking cause may not be identified in all cases, it will be a great help to eliminate it when it can be pinpointed. You can discover what may be contributing to your child's thumbsucking habit by looking openly and honestly at your child and your family situation. Perhaps there are too many demands being placed on the child, or the child needs more time with the parents. Perhaps the child is shy and needs to move slowly into social situations. Or the child is expected to be quiet too much of the time. Perhaps someone is being too critical, or the child is too busy with scheduled activities.

Perhaps a parent prefers to let the child continue thumbsucking because it helps him sleep. Or the parent is afraid that stopping will damage the child psychologically. Perhaps there has been a big change in the child's life and he needs time to adjust.

We must eliminate those things that cause or confound the thumbsucking habit. In the ideal situation, all factors that make the thumbsucking habit more complex are eliminated before or during the process.

Talk to Someone

Find a sympathetic friend, relative, religious leader, or therapist with whom you can discuss this issue openly and honestly. The individual you select could be almost anyone, as long as they have an open heart and a willing ear. You will need to get this out on occasion, and it will help to have someone with whom you can vent and brainstorm. Just talking about it will bring peace and clarity. But don't whine.

Talking about troublesome issues in one's life helps put things into perspective and helps to organize those fuzzy thoughts we all have when things just aren't going the way we think they should.

Look to Your Religion

Religion offers a family a set of rules to follow that, truth be told, make life better. A family who believes in a personal God and who teaches their children about God's desires can apply the principles described in their religion to help them shape all their children's behaviors, including a thumbsucking habit.

For example, a child can pray to God on a regular basis for courage to stop thumbsucking or to help other children in the family not to tease the thumbsucker. Or he could thank God for help when successful. There are going to be obstacles that the family must face. Praying as a family through this time can help keep everyone focused on the plan and procedures.

Be Patient

All habits are difficult to break, so be patient as you wait for your child to change. Children learn new skills over time, not overnight. Once a child is introduced to the idea, it may take several months for him to commit to breaking the habit. Then, once the child commits to the process, it may take him a while to begin. And it may take him a while to get through it. Remind yourself how long it takes to help a child learn other basic skills. For example, how long does it take a child to learn to tie his shoes? Don't rush your child into the process, and don't rush him through it once he begins. Although some children can eliminate an oral habit overnight given the right circumstances, others require time.

Summary

The eleven guidelines for beginning the treatment process reveal that thumbsucking must be treated as a behavior and that parents must make a firm decision, work at an appropriate pace, and adopt a positive attitude in attempting to change it. Children must be allowed to help make this decision at a certain age, but parents can talk them into it. Parents should examine possible causes of thumbsucking and should find someone with whom this issue can be discussed. In addition, families should look to their religion for help and be patient throughout the process.

Chapter 4

The General Plan

Getting Organized for Success

Now that we have laid our foundation, it is time to create the plan and to implement the procedures and activities themselves. Some of the ideas offered in the next few chapters are simple discussions that can take place during the course of everyday living. Other ideas are activities that should be scheduled. These activities include lighthearted approaches and downright drastic measures. Although many of the ideas in these chapters are useful for young children, others will be applied more appropriately to older ones.

The following are preliminary strategies for how to introduce the child to the idea of eliminating his thumb-sucking habit. It explains how to make a definitive plan of action. The material includes four sections:

1. Identify the problem
2. Give information
3. Select an elimination period
4. Make and write a plan

Identify the Problem

To start, investigate the mouth, the thumb, and the process of growing up. As children learn more about the mouth and the thumb and about outgrowing infantile behaviors, they can begin to formulate ideas about why they should stop sucking their thumbs. These discoveries then become the leverage for making a plan.

Characterize the Thumb

Take a few moments to help the child discover his thumb: what it looks like, how big it is, how it is placed on the hand, how it moves, the skin on the thumb, the thumbnail, and so forth. If the child sucks one thumb and not the other, compare the two. The sucked thumb often will look different: red, wet, or even swollen, shriveled, or calloused. Make sure the child understands the difference between wet and dry. Talk about the skin and what dry skin looks like compared to wet skin.

Explore the Mouth

Help the child explore his own mouth. This can be done at a mirror while he brushes his teeth, or at any time when a mirror is handy. Use the mirror to look in the mouth with a flashlight or penlight that will illuminate the dark cavity and make the discoveries more fun. Name each part of the mouth as you discover them together: lips, teeth, gums, tongue, palate (roof of the mouth), uvula (the "punching bag" in the back), throat, tonsils (if present), and papillae (taste buds) on the back of the tongue. Notice each bump, rough spot, dark spot, ridge, or any other unusual feature of the mouth. Talk about how interesting the mouth is, and compare and contrast your adult mouth with your child's.

Take a few moments to talk about what goes in the mouth and what does *not* go in the mouth.

Food, toothbrushes, dental floss, toothpicks, braces, retainers, bubble gum, whistles, horns, harmonicas, balloons, and so forth go in the mouth; hands and fingers rarely go in the mouth.

Ask Advice of the Dentist or Orthodontist

A trip to the dentist or orthodontist will provide even more information about the teeth and their structure. Ask the dental specialist to explain to your child how thumbsucking might affect the teeth. Sometimes a single visit to a dentist who knows what to say is just the right thing to motivate the child to stop thumbsucking overnight!

Visit the Speech and Language Pathologist

Some speech and language pathologists specialize in thumbsucking problems and their relationships to the development of teeth, speech, and swallowing. Typically, these therapists work in private practice. This kind of speech and language specialist will be able to give your child a lot of information about thumbsucking and good reasons to quit the habit.

See an Orofacial Myofunctional Therapist

An orofacial myofunctional therapist (OMT) is a professional with special expertise in eliminating inappropriate oral habits, including thumbsucking. Speech-language pathologists, dental professionals, and others also can attain this area of expertise. The trained orofacial myofunctional therapist is one of the best professionals to visit to discuss the issue of thumbsucking. They are thoroughly equipped to handle thumbsucking problems and will provide a great source of information and support for you and your child.

Measure the Child's Development

Take measurements of your child's height, weight, shoe size, and clothing size. Make a chart to compare the child's current size with prior years. Talk about how big the child is getting. Discuss birthdays and the way in which the child is growing year after year. Discuss the fact that when a child gets bigger, he is less dependent on the things he did when he was younger. Talk about how he used to ride a tricycle, wear diapers, take naps, drink bottles, and so forth but he doesn't anymore. Help your child understand that he is growing and with growth comes changes in behavior.

Look at Other Children

You probably have been told at least once not to compare your child to other children, but in this case it may be helpful. Encourage your child to think about or watch other children his own age or older. Help him see that most children his own age and older do not suck the thumb. Then, point out a smaller child who does suck the thumb. Compare and contrast your child with these children.

Give Information

Early in the process, your child will need information about thumbsucking in order to be encouraged to eliminate the habit. He needs to know what's wrong.

- GIVE DIRECT INSTRUCTION: Children typically need to be told directly what is and what is not expected of them. For example, "It is not appropriate to suck the thumb."
- DESCRIBE THE PROBLEM: State the problem in terms your child can understand. For example, "You are too big to suck your thumb."
- GIVE INFORMATION: Explain what is happening as a result of thumbsucking. For example, "Your thumb is getting chapped because you put it in your mouth and get it all wet."

- TALK ABOUT APPEARANCE: Describe how your child appears to other children and adults when he sucks the thumb. For example, "David thinks you look like a baby when you suck your thumb."
- MODEL AND DESCRIBE APPROPRIATE BEHAVIORS: Make comments to your child about behaviors you expect. For example, "I expect you to keep your thumb out of your mouth while we wait for the bus."
- TALK ABOUT HEALTH RISKS: Be truthful about the risks of putting hands and fingers in the mouth. Talk to your pharmacist about pinworms and other parasites. Pick up a few brochures about their transmission, prevention, and medical treatment. Share this with your child.
- TALK ABOUT SWALLOWING: If your child has a swallowing problem or difference associated with thumbsucking, it should be discussed with a professional. Use the information described in chapter 1 for general information, and seek a professional for help.
- TALK ABOUT SPEECH: If your child has a speech or language problem associated with thumbsucking, it should be discussed with the help of a professional. Use the information described in chapter 1 for general information, and seek a professional for help.
- LET THE CHILD READ THIS: This book may be an excellent one for older children to read. Use discretion and encourage him to read one section at a time. Then discuss the contents together. Prepare a summary of the book to share with other family members.
- MODEL THUMBSUCKING: Scrub your hands in front of your child and model thumbsucking. Let him see you do it. Parental thumbsucking looks really bad to children once they get

over the humor of it. Your child will not want to see you suck your thumb in front of his friends. This can be a nice way to start discouraging thumbsucking in front of others.

- DO A WORKBOOK: Consider using a workbook with your child to teach him how to eliminate a thumbsucking habit in a systematic way. One good workbook is entitled *My Thumb and I.* It is a systematic 10-step program to help eliminate a thumbsucking habit. (See ordering information listed in the appendix.)

- READ CHILDREN'S BOOKS: There are a few children's books appropriate for eliminating a thumbsucking habit. They inform and comfort young children about making these life-changing decisions.

  ◊ *David Decides* is an older book with a story about an elementary-age boy who decides not to suck his thumb anymore

  ◊ *The Habit*, with the Berenstain Bears, is the story of how Sister Bear decides to stop biting her fingernails. The general storyline can be adapted easily to thumbsucking and other oral habits

  ◊ *Bye-Bye, Pacifier* and *Bye-Bye, Thumbsucking* are Golden Books especially appropriate for very young children

Select an Elimination Period

Thumbsucking has to stop at some point. "Maybe we'll do it next week" isn't going to work. Your child isn't going to stop someday; he has to stop on a certain day or during a certain week. When parents and children select a final date of thumbsucking and then plan to stick with that decision, success can be achieved.

Make and Write a Plan

As you begin to help your child eliminate a thumbsucking habit, design a general action plan. An action plan contains three main parts: goals, procedures, and outcomes. You can generate this plan alone, especially if your child is very young, or you and your child can develop it together.

Goals

The goal for most children will be to eliminate the thumbsucking habit. The goal should be specific and positive. Don't simply state, "Johnny will never suck his thumb again." That is too general. Instead, create a goal that will specify exactly what the child will accomplish, such as, "Johnny will fall asleep seven nights in a row without sucking his thumb." That tells *what* (Johnny will fall asleep), *how* (without sucking his thumb), and to what *criteria* (seven nights in a row). The goal must tell how the child will succeed.

Procedures

Next, your plan should contain a list of procedures that will achieve the goal. Think through the problem alone or with your child, and make a list of tools and activities. Choose any of the ideas presented in the next chapter for your list. Select the best alternatives for your child, personalize them according to your lifestyle, and use them.

Your list might specify a four-step nighttime routine:

1. Wash hands and lotion them before bed
2. Put glove on
3. Talk and pray with Daddy about stopping my thumbsucking
4. Sleep on my back with my hands at my sides

Brainstorm your list at first; then boil it down to a master plan and post it prominently. Put it on the refrigerator or in a visible place in the child's room.

Determine who will be privy to this plan. Decide if siblings need to know it. It may be important that a grandparent knows for overnights, or for a babysitter to know for a night when the parents will be gone. It also may be important that friends and buddies do *not* know, but it may be important that their parents know for times when the child plays at their house. Some children will be very specific about who they do and do not want to know what's going on. Try to honor each of their requests, but don't be afraid to talk this over with your child and to add people to the list when necessary.

Outcomes

Finally, your plan will contain information about the end result and the rewards. List the outcomes on the bottom of the procedures list. For example, write: "After seven nights, I will not have to wear the glove anymore. And on Saturday morning Mommy will give me a big hug and Daddy will take me to get a new game!"

Write a Plan

Make your plan a reality both to you and to your child by putting it down on paper. This written plan should include all the important elements. If your child is quite young, you will want to fill this out on your own and use it for your own guideline. If your child is old enough to be an active part of the elimination process, you will want him to help you fill it out so that both you and he will be clear about what you are doing.

Select a time during which you and your child can have a quiet opportunity to answer the questions. You don't have to complete the form in one sitting; it can be completed during two or three times together. And there may be more than one answer to some of the questions. Use the form as a springboard for discussions, but make sure to specify answers to the questions. Also, make sure your child understands that answers can change over time as the process unfolds. The written plan gives you a framework from which to operate, and it will help motivate you when needed. A sample thumbsucking plan appears below.

The length of time it takes to eliminate an oral habit depends upon many factors:

- The adult's motivational skills and relationship with the child
- The frequency of application and the adult's diligence
- The adult's ability to introduce new ideas and the child's willingness to let the adult teach
- The child's intelligence and awareness levels

─────────── ❖ ───────────

Summary

At some point, it is time to start the process of eliminating a thumbsucking habit. Alone or with the help of the child, the parent can write a plan that includes goals, procedures, outcomes, and timeframes. Parents are encouraged to give basic information to their children to help them discover the thumb and the mouth, and to learn why not to suck the thumb.

The Thumbsucking Plan

Name: _____ Date: _____

I suck my thumb (check all that apply):

__at night   __in class   __at school
__at recess   __when nervous __when reading
__when bored __in the car   __when scared
__watching TV __during naps   __other

My goal is to:

I want to stop sucking my thumb because:

I will reach my goal by (date):

The people who will know about this will be:

My treasured object will be put:

Rules I will follow are:

Reminders that will be used are:

Things I can do instead of sucking my thumb:

So I don't suck my thumb at night I will:

Things to remind me not to suck my thumb are:

The reward for not sucking my thumb will be:

I will get my treasured object back when:

Chapter 5

Activities and Techniques

The Nuts and Bolts of Change

If you think this chapter is where all the really good ideas are, you're right! While prior chapters revealed reasons to eliminate habitual thumbsucking or other oral habits, as well as guidelines, principles, and plans for approaching and organizing this topic with your child, this chapter gives you the nuts and bolts of how to change an oral habit. It includes activities and techniques to combat all aspects of this behavior.

Bedtime Routines

One of the main issues in eliminating a thumbsucking habit is to decide what to do about sleep time, because most children who suck the thumb do so at night. Parents need to determine at what level of intensity the thumbsucking habit is to be addressed. The nighttime approach for infants and toddlers should be quite different than the one for older children. Let's look at these differences.

For Infants and Toddlers

For an infant or toddler, parents may decide to allow the child to fall asleep with the thumb in the mouth but then to remove it once the child drifts off to sleep. Try to pull it out without waking him. If the lips are parted slightly and the thumb is not being actively sucked, simply slip the thumb out carefully. If that doesn't work, try removing it quickly. Once the thumb is removed, place your hand reassuringly on the child's head, chest, or back to settle him again.

If the child is sucking hard on the thumb or has stopped sucking but is still firmly drawing the thumb into the mouth, pulling it out will cause a *pop* as suction is broken. Often, this will disturb a sleeping child. If so, gently pull one lip away from the thumb to break the seal, and then slip the thumb out.

For Older Children

An older child will have to face the issue of thumbsucking to go to sleep more directly and will need help making a plan for stopping the nighttime habit. The key to this aspect of the program is to decide what will help the child remember not to suck and what will help prevent him from sucking during the night. This usually means placing some type of device on the thumb, hand, or arm that will alert him that he is about to put the thumb in the mouth. This will prevent him from sucking or will make it unpleasant to do so. A plan can be made and enacted once the older child has some understanding that thumbsucking is detrimental. He also must understand it is a habit that is his responsibility to stop.

Gadgets and Gizmos

Facing the issue may not be sufficient enough for a child to eliminate a thumbsucking habit. Sometimes an object can keep the thumb from going in the mouth by preventing the child from being able to suck on the thumb or by providing an adverse reaction to thumbsucking. Preventative measures can be especially important when we begin to design nighttime routines. During the night, there is no way to guarantee that your child will keep the thumb out of the mouth. Once the light is out and parents retreat to other parts of the house, the child who sucks the thumb is free to do so. A system must be designed to prevent thumbsucking in bed. The system must be safe for the child and it must be tolerable. Here are several suggestions.

Gloves and Cutout Gloves

Gloves or mittens on the hands are excellent thumbsucking-prevention devices. Therefore, professionals often recommend using cutout gloves. Take a child's thin glove and cut off all the fingers, but leave the thumb on the glove. When the child places the new funny-looking glove on his hand, it will cover the palm, the back of the hand, and the thumb, but it will leave the rest of the fingers exposed.

With the glove in place on the hand, the child is ready for bed. Tell him why the glove is there—to remind him not to suck—and that he should leave it on all night. Many children will tolerate the glove in place and will be able to break the nighttime habit by using it. (See appendix.)

Thumb Guards

Another idea to prevent nighttime thumbsucking is to use a thumb guard. A thumb guard is a plastic or metal thumb cup that is fastened with white tape to the thumb and is typically used to protect the thumb when it is broken or sprained. A thumb guard worn for a thumbsucking habit allows the thumb to be placed in the mouth but does not allow the thumb to be sucked. Children typically will not suck on the plastic or metal. Thumb guards can be purchased wherever first-aid supplies are offered. (See appendix.)

Elbow Wraps

Elbow wraps don't prevent a child from sucking the thumb, but merely provide a reminder each time he is about to. Wind an Ace bandage or other piece of cloth tightly around the elbow—not so tight that it stops circulation, but tight enough to feel a little uncomfortable when the elbow is bent. This restriction reminds the child not to bend the arm and, subsequently, not to put the thumb in the mouth.

Yucky-Tasting Stuff

Put on like nail polish, these products are made to be a strong reminder against thumbsucking and nail biting. Ask your pharmacist for a recommendation. These nasty-tasting products are not meant to punish the child, and they cannot absolutely prevent thumbsucking, because they wear off in a few hours. They just give a negative impression each time he puts the thumb in his mouth. One yucky-tasting alternative is to use water mixed with cayenne pepper.

Other Reminders

Because it is so hard to remember to keep the thumb out of the mouth at all times, it is helpful to use a few other reminders: visible objects, pictures, stickers, cards, or written words that are placed in strategic locations. For example, a tiny card with the word *thumb* written or drawn on it could be easily visible in the car by fastening it to the back of the front seat. Here are some other ideas:

- RINGS: Get a special ring for the child to wear. Teach him that the ring is intended as a reminder not to suck. Do not use these with children who will suck them off and swallow them.

- POSTED REWARDS: Tape a picture of the long-term reward (suggestions below) on the refrigerator or next to the child's bed. This will act as a daily reminder of what he is trying to achieve.

- STICKERS: Place relevant stickers on notebooks, inside lockers, on pencils, on mirrors, on doorframes, in the lunchboxes—anywhere your child is sure to look during an average day. Stickers of hands, lips, balloons, thumbs up, and so forth can be used as a reminder as long as the child understands the association. The fun part about stickers is that other children and adults will not know that the sticker has special significance.

- REMINDERS ON THE THUMB: Place a tiny sticker, a star, or a dot on the thumb. When the child places the thumb in the mouth he will be reminded gently to take it out. Other children and adults do not have to know why the tiny item is there. Do not use these with children who will suck them off and swallow them.

- BAND-AID OR TAPE ON THE THUMB: Professionals also recommended the subtle reminders of Band-Aids, adhesive tape, or gauze tape on the thumb to help deter sucking. They are not pleasant to suck. Caution: Bandages or tape on the thumb could be dangerous if sucked off! Parents should use extreme caution and avoid this completely if the child is in danger of sucking it off the thumb.

- SPECIAL PRODUCTS: There are a few companies that sell stickers, cups, bookmarks, wristbands, figurines, erasers, rubber stamps, key rings, and other paraphernalia that is specifically designed to remind a child not to suck the thumb or engage in other oral habits. These products are cute, unobtrusive, and generally inexpensive. (See appendix.)

Rules

An easy way to get a message across to one particular child in the family without making him stand out is to make blanket rules that apply to everyone. These family rules can be shared with other children who come to play at the home and won't single-out the thumbsucker.

No Hands or Fingers in the Mouth

Establish a rule that no children, under any condition, are to put their hands or fingers in their mouths. The only exception to this rule is for children under two years of age, who are still mouthing. Teach your children to use napkins, toothpicks, and dental floss to remove unwanted food from the mouths and teeth. Teach them to wash their hands before eating and to keep their hands away from their faces and mouths. Talk about germs, dirt, and parasites as a way to solidify that this is not just a crazy rule, but one which has merit.

No Suck Zone

Establish clear locations within your home that are places where no sucking should occur. For example, you could outlaw sucking at the table, in bed, at the computer, on the couch, in front of the TV, or in the car. Make sure your children know exactly where these places are. It gives the message that you don't want wet thumbs in your house and you don't like wet hands on your furniture.

Rules Presented with Strong Emphasis

Use a strong "I mean it" tone to get your child's attention. Do not threaten, but consider acting mean—it will not destroy your child's ego. For example, say, "I said *no*! Stop it! Keep your hands away from your face! Next time, you will be punished." Firm tones help your child understand that you mean business and that *your* limit is *the* limit. Set the limit and hold it consistently. Don't cower if your child says, "You're mean."

Rules Presented with Light Emphasis
Make soft statements about the rules. Explain that these rules are not intended to suppress family fun, but that everyone in the family must abide by them. Tease your child into repeating the rule that he already knows. For example, "Just what was that rule about thumbsucking? Let's see, I wonder if I can remember it. I can't seem to remember it. You can't possibly remember it, can you?"

Choices about Following Rules
State your household rule and give the child a choice about whether to follow it or to take a less desirable course of action. For example, say, "No sucking with me. You can sit next to me during the show or we can turn the TV off. It's your choice."

If the child says, "Neither!" simply choose the less desirable choice for him and let him know that next time he can choose differently if he likes.

Activities

Children often suck the thumb because they are bored. In today's society, children also suck their thumbs when they are idly sitting in the car, in class, in front of a computer, or watching television. An antidote is to get the body, mind, and hands busy. Children love to do all kinds of things! Suggestions in the following sections will get you going.

Small Toys
Certain small toys are conducive to busying both hands together, like building with Lego's, stringing beads, or dressing dolls. These types of activities get the child's hands busy and encourage the thumb to come out of the mouth.

Solo Games

Many small, solo-play games and toys are available to occupy children's hands and minds when they are in confined places, like handheld electronic games or small toys with tiny parts. You don't need to run out and buy a bunch of new toys and games, but look through what your child already has and pick out a few that he has not played with for a while. Put them up somewhere so you can have quick access to them for those special times when your child needs to busy the hands instead of thumbsuck. Consider keeping games or toys in the car at all times, or let him pick one to bring for each trip.

Group Games

How about Graveyard? In Graveyard, all the children lie on the floor or ground and remain perfectly still, as if they were dead bodies in a graveyard. The adult or designated child walks around the graveyard looking for any child who moves even the slightest amount. Any child caught moving is out of the game. The last child lying down is the winner. The winner gets to be the patrol for the next game and so forth.

Arts and Crafts

Drawing, painting, coloring, pasting, gluing, glittering, stringing beads, modeling with clay, and sewing are just a few of the hundreds of projects children enjoy in the area of arts and crafts. Each one will keep the hands busy. You may want to have a new project waiting in the wings for that special moment when the child really needs it.

Chores

Not always your child's favorite activity, but doing chores is an excellent way to busy the hands. "I need someone to set the table" may be all you have to say to get your child's hands busy. Make the chore fun by letting the child set the table however he sees fit—with paper plates, fancy dishes, hand-drawn place cards, or fancy goblets. Let him set an outdoor table in good weather. Helping with household or kitchen chores busies the hands as the child peels, washes, or wipes.

Manicures

For most girls, attending to the nails is an excellent distraction from sucking the thumb. Boys also enjoy a limited amount of manicuring when presented under the right conditions. Clean, clip and file, polish, and paint the nails—or just paint the nails. Or let your child paint her nails by herself, make a mess, remove the polish, and then you can paint them neatly. Painted nails busy the hands and encourage the child to keep the hands out of the mouth. Paint the nails at night when the child is in bed so that she has to lie still with hands at her sides as she falls asleep.

Lotion the Hands

To help break the habit, put lotion on several times a day. It provides a soothing feeling, brings attention to the hands, busies the hands, and discourages thumbsucking because of its unpleasant taste.

Massage the Hands and Fingers

Give your child a hand and finger massage with lotion or oil to soothe the hands and distract from thumbsucking. Use this as a time to talk about and make discoveries about the hands, fingers, and thumbs.

Negative Practice

One way to help reduce an undesirable behavior is to have the child do more of it at times. In this way, the habit comes to his attention, he gains some early control of it (it's easier to do more of a bad habit than to do less of it), and he may get a little sick of it. You might insist that your child suck his thumb during an entire movie without stopping, or you might explain that while the rest of the family is having dessert, you expect him to sit on the couch and suck his thumb. He'll beg and plead to be allowed to eat the desert. Then combine this with an incentive. Say, for example: "If you do not suck your thumb for the rest of the evening, you may have your dessert before bed."

List Your Options

Discuss with your child what he can do instead of sucking the thumb, and write the ideas down in your plan. Post the list and use it as a resource for ideas when one is needed. Over time, add new ideas to the list and remove those that are inappropriate, unused, or generally not really of interest to your child. Consider making situation-specific lists, such as a list for use at Grandma's house.

Special Stimuli

Normalize Oral-Tactile Sensitivity

Some children with oral habits have concurrent oral-tactile sensitivity problems. Some are overly sensitive to touch in the mouth, while others are less sensitive. Typically, hypersensitive children do not like to put certain food textures or objects, such as toothbrushes, into their mouths. Children who are hyposensitive usually love to put anything into their mouths.

When children have oral sensory problems, they sometimes develop oral habits in order to satisfy cravings they have for oral stimulation. In treatment, therapists grade the presentation of oral stimuli in order to normalize the child's oral sensitivity. To normalize oral-tactile sensitivity levels, they regularly use foods, objects with various consistencies and textures, and vibration and temperature variations in and on the mouth one or more times per week. This therapy can help decrease mouthing behavior, thumbsucking, and other oral habits. If your child is working with a speech-language pathologist, occupational therapist, or physical therapist, consult with these professionals about oral sensitivity before applying stimulation.

Use Cold Stimulation
Cold foods and play items can be excellent for curbing an oral habit in children who are seeking oral stimulation. A cold stimulus brings more of the sensation they are seeking. Plus, it can soothe the hypersensitive oral-tactile system and increase sensation in the hyposensitive one. Cold stimuli includes ice cubes, ice shavings, ice pops, frozen bananas, ice cream, milkshakes, ice chips, frozen yogurt, cold apple sauce, ice water, or frozen juice made in a small paper cup.

Use Vibration
Children with oral sensitivity problems also may enjoy vibration in and around the mouth. Many toys that vibrate, such as vibrating balls and other rubber toys, are available in toy stores. Certain vibrating massage equipment also is appropriate for putting in and on the mouth. And any rubber toy can be taped or affixed with a rubber band to a vibrator and then mouthed. Make sure the item cannot be ingested. Vibration given at regular intervals may help normalize oral-tactile sensitivity, decreasing the need for oral stimulation. As a result, thumbsucking behavior may be reduced.

Children with oral hypersensitivity react in different, often strong ways to powerful stimuli such as ice or vibration. Make sure to consult with your speech-language pathologist or occupational or physical therapist about how these techniques can be used with your child. Do not use vibration on children with seizure disorders or hypertonicity without first consulting a qualified professional.

Stimulate the Proprioceptive System

The proprioceptive system is that unconscious neurological system that allows the brain to understand how muscles and joints are working within the body. When the proprioceptive system is poorly developed or disorganized, children sometimes seek proprioceptive input to the body in different places. One place where they sometimes seek stimulation is in the mouth. Children seeking this type of stimulation often have chewing habits. They may chew on shirtsleeves, collars, toys, pencils, or chew on thumbs intermittently as they suck them. Children needing oral proprioceptive stimulation need appropriate objects on which to chew in order to stimulate the muscles and joints of the mouth. The best substance is rubber. Large rubber toys and rubber tubing are the most economical, easily available, and appropriate objects. Infant teething toys, available in your local grocery or drugstore, also are very useful. Rubber tubing can be purchased in hardware or aquarium stores. Some doggie chew toys work great too.

Collect a supply of appropriate rubber objects, wash them, and place them in a container. Mark the container with the child's name or write "Chew Toys" or "Mouth Toys" on the outside. Allow the child access to these items at certain intervals, say once or twice per day or several times per week. Do not let these toys get intermixed with the rest of his toys. Have your child play with them while sitting or lying in a certain place, and put them away when he is done. Set up a mirror in front of the child so he can watch himself. Encourage him to bite and chew with vigor. (See appendix.)

Offer Rewards

Eliminating a thumbsucking habit should be rewarded because it is hard work. Everyone receives some type of reward for work done well. Hard-working adults are rewarded with paychecks, and hard-working students are rewarded with good grades. The work of eliminating a thumbsucking habit is worth a reward. Sometimes this reward is tangible, like a new game or an overnight party. Other times, this reward is nothing more than a closer relationship between the parent and the child. Who can say which type is better? Some children need tangible rewards to understand their success while others do not. Rewards are given throughout the process of change and again at the end of the program. Rewards can be immediate, short term, or long term.

Immediate Rewards

Immediate rewards are those given on the spot. They keep the process going forward. When a young child puts his hands down as you pick him up, you can give him an immediate reward by saying with pride, "You put your hands down!" Give him a hug, a smile, a kiss, a thumbs-up sign, or an I-love-you sign with lots of eye contact. Loving intimacies make the best immediate rewards.

Short-Term Rewards

Good short-term rewards are those that draw you and your child closer together while also delivering the clear message that the child is making progress. For example, "You didn't suck your thumb the entire time we waited for Daddy! Very good! You have earned having a friend stay overnight. Who will it be?" Short-term rewards do not signal the end of the program; they signal that the child is doing well *in* the program. Therefore, they do not need to be huge.

Long-Term Rewards

The long-term reward is the biggest one. It is offered when the target goal has been met, signaling the end of the process and success by the child. Long-term rewards are never given before thumbsucking is completely eliminated. Don't be tempted to give the reward if the child did not achieve his goal, even if he tried very hard. Offer a different reward for trying, but do not give the final reward before the child actually succeeds in eliminating the thumbsucking habit. If you do, you will completely undermine your attempts. Talk with your child about the long-term reward. Together, pick something meaningful. Do not tie the long-term reward to any other behavior. It is reserved solely for success in the thumbsucking elimination program.

SAMPLE LONG-TERM REWARDS

- Game or toy
- A dress
- Movie night
- Weekend vacation
- Overnight party
- Magazine subscription
- Trip to a museum
- Manicure set
- Telephone
- Swimming party
- Horseback ride
- Camping trip
- New swing set
- Puppy
- New bike
- CD collection

Bribes

A bribe is something given before an event in order to convince or cajole. For example, if you were to take your child to a movie in order to get him to stop sucking the thumb, the movie trip would be a bribe. It would not be a reward for stopping the behavior. Bribes do not work in most cases. It is recommended that you stay away from them. Immediate, short-term, and long-term rewards work much better.

Treasured Objects

Oftentimes a child has an object, such as a blanket or stuffed animal, that he holds as he sucks the thumb. It is very difficult to eliminate a thumbsucking habit when that object is still accessible. It is as if the object itself draws out the thumbsucking behavior. The thumbsucking behavior and the loved object are intricately intertwined, making it difficult to separate one from the other. In order to help your child eliminate thumbsucking, the object which is paired with thumbsucking must be set aside. This is not to say that the adored object should be discarded. Rather, it can be placed out of reach and made inaccessible for a while.

Make a special time or ceremony out of putting the treasured object away. Launder, fold, and place it in a special container like a gift box, or wrap it with special paper and then place it in a forbidden area high in a closet or in the attic. Treat the object with the respect it deserves, and reassure your child that he can have it back at a later time.

Some children may be allowed to check the favorite object at various times throughout the thumbsucking elimination period or while awaiting its return. Checking the object may assure him that it still exists and that it is safe. The child may show no real need to have the object back, and seeing it will cause no problems. Other children, however, may be unable to check the object, because it will cause too much emotion about its loss. The mere sight of it may trigger a return to thumbsucking. You know your child better than anyone else, so think about this and use common sense in determining whether or not to visit the object.

In planning to store the treasured object, make sure to specify when it can be returned and write this in your plan. It is suggested that the object not be returned immediately upon reaching the elimination goal. The hastened reunion of the child and his object may trigger a quick retreat into thumbsucking. Instead, set a return time fairly far in the future. One year is necessary for many children. If, for example, the thumbsucking elimination routine begins just after the child's seventh birthday, the plan might be to return the object to the child on his eighth birthday. The object might be offered as a present at that time. When you return the object, praise your child for his yearlong wait and discuss his remarkable growth during that period.

Like holding treasured objects, children often engage in other soothing behaviors while they suck the thumb. Some children twirl the hair, rub a cheek or thigh, or stroke two fingers together. These behaviors also must stop during the elimination period.

Rest Time

Rest time is a time to be quiet and do something by oneself. Rest time is not necessarily for naps. It is simply a time to be quiet and to do quiet activities. Rest time is a primary thumbsucking opportunity for children with oral habits, so it is important to think through quiet activities that can your child can do. Reading, drawing, playing with a small toy or object, and some of the less involved arts and crafts projects described above are excellent sources of down-time activity. The key is to have something to do while not really doing anything, so that the body and mind can rest. Another idea is to have the child stimulate the mouth in other ways at this time. Let the child suck on an ice pop or chew gum during a rest time on a comfortable chair. In this way, he will busy the hands, stimulate the mouth, and rest all at the same time.

Teasing

Teasing helps children become aware of their behaviors in a fun way. For example, say, "I saw that thumb go in your mouth! The tickle monster is going to get you! The tickle monster doesn't like children to suck their thumbs!" These types of activities may momentarily increase your child's oral behavior as he tries to engage in the fun. That's OK. It will help the child become aware of and begin to gain some control over the behavior. Reserve teasing play for special times or for when the atmosphere around the house has been a little gloomy.

Timeframes

Young children may have difficulty understanding time, how much is "too much," or how often is "too often." Relate the child's sucking to time. For example, say, "You only sucked your thumb for five minutes today while we rode in the car to get Jennifer. Then you stopped. That's great! That means that you didn't suck your thumb for most of the day—only for a little while."

Hands Down and No Sucking Times

Encourage your child to take his thumb out of his mouth for specific time periods. Say, for example, "You may not suck your thumb while we ride to school" or, ". . . are in the store" or, " . . . while we wait for your mom." Gradually increase the length of these periods, and increase the number of times throughout the day in which you initiate them. Don't be afraid to make big leaps in these time segments by saying something like, "Starting now, your job is to keep your hands down until I serve dinner, during dinner, and after dinner until bedtime."

Allowable Sucking Periods

As crazy as it may seem, it can be helpful for your child to have specific times or situations during which he may suck, like after lunch. This will help him gain a little more control over the habit as he learns to put off self-gratification. Gradually reduce and shorten these allowable sucking times to prevent distress. However, if used for too long, your ability to eliminate the behavior completely will be undermined.

Time Limits

Set a limit on acceptable time periods. For example, "You may suck for three minutes. Then I want you to find something else to do." Or set a timer and say, "When the timer goes off, you will be all done sucking. Then you must find something else to do."

Songs

Songs help us remember things. Almost every child memorizes the entire twenty-six letters of the alphabet by learning the ABC song. Advertisers use songs to market products. Remember the Oscar Meyer Wiener song? "Oh, I wish I were an Oscar Meyer Wiener . . ." Just as songs increase our awareness about certain products, they also can help us buy into the idea of eliminating a thumbsucking habit. Take any tune, make up your own words, and you have a song about thumbsucking that can favorably influence your child.

I'm Never Gonna Suck My Thumb
(Sung to the tune of the Oscar Meyer Wiener song.)

Oh, I'm never gonna' suck my thumb.
That is something I will never do.
'Cause if I go and suck my thumb,
It will turn all yellow, red, and blue!

DJ Had a Great Big Thumb
(Sung to the tune of "Mary Had a Little Lamb.")

DJ had a great big thumb, great big thumb, great big thumb.
DJ had a great big thumb. He kept it in his mouth.

And everywhere that DJ went, DJ went, DJ went,
Everywhere that DJ went, his mother told him, "Out!"

His thumb got very wet and red, wet and red, wet and red,
His thumb got very wet and red each day he was at school.

It made the children laugh and tease, laugh and tease, laugh and tease.
It made the children laugh and tease to see it in his mouth.

So, DJ decided to keep it out, keep it out, keep it out.
DJ decided to keep it out because he was so cool!

Brain Ticklers

Word Associations

Teach your child a word-association technique to remember not to suck the thumb. For example, select a word that is seen commonly in the child's environment, like *exit*. Then make up a rhyme or phrase that will remind him not to suck every time he sees the word: "Exit means go out the door. I will suck my thumb no more."

Heroes

Use your child's interest in heroes or superheroes to remind him not to suck the thumb. For example, if your child is fascinated with Batman, teach him that every time he thinks of Batman, plays with his toy Batman, sees a Batman commercial, draws a Batman figure, puts on his Batman cape, drives his Batman car, or plays with his deck of Batman cards, he should check himself to see if he has his thumb in his mouth because Batman never sucks his thumb!

Summary

There are a wide variety of practical activities for eliminating a thumbsucking habit through night-time and rest-time routines; establishing family rules; getting the hands busy; using negative practice; normalizing oral-tactile sensitivity; stimulating the proprioceptive system; offering rewards; putting aside an associated treasured object; using reminder systems; and using songs, objects, and time to your advantage.

Chapter 6

Talking with Your Child

Staying Connected During the Process of Change

It is critical to talk to children about thumbsucking in a way that encourages the learning process. By taking on this assignment, we become the child's mentors on the topic of thumbsucking. So, what we say is important.

How should you talk with your child about his thoughts and feelings before, during, and after eliminating a thumbsucking habit? It's important to praise him throughout the process. The following five sections include information on how to talk to your child in loving ways, in ways that inform him, and in ways that lift him up.

1. Answer questions
2. Express feelings
3. Praise the child
4. Use disapproval
5. Show respect for the child's dilemma

Answer Questions

Your child may ask, "Why can't I suck my thumb?"

Don't rush to answer that question. Instead, turn the questioning back to the child by asking, "What do you think?" That gives him an opportunity to express what he thinks is going on.

He might say, "Because my thumb gets red" or, "Because my teeth will grow funny." Your child's answer will give you information on what he knows about the thumbsucking problem. Use this as a beginning point in treatment. Then you can continue to shape his understanding of the issue by adding more information.

Some children have the wrong idea about why they should not suck the thumb. An inappropriate answer, such as, "Because I'm bad," suggests the child needs mature ideas about thumbsucking.

First, a child will need reassurance that everything is all right. Then he will need some more relevant and useful information, like, "Oh, honey, you are not bad. You are a good boy and I love you very much. But sucking your thumb is not good for your mouth. It can make your teeth grow crooked. Mommy wants your teeth to be as straight as possible, so it's time to think about how we can stop this sucking."

Sometimes children find the best answers from another adult they trust. For example, a parent might say: "I don't think sucking your thumb is good for your teeth. Let's see what Grandpa says. He loves you very much. I bet he knows why you should stop sucking your thumb."

Express Feelings

Thumbsucking can be an emotional issue for both parent and child, and sometimes these emotions should be aired. Such outbursts can be avoided when a child knows he can express himself on the topic of sucking the thumb.

- BE A MIRROR OF YOUR CHILD'S FEELINGS: Don't ignore feelings about eliminating thumbsucking.

Children are comforted when they know their parents understand. Say, "I know it's hard to stop. You want to suck that thumb so badly!"

- ENCOURAGE STRENGTH: If your child falters, offer him words of encouragement, "You can do it. You're big enough. I know it's hard, but you didn't suck your thumb last night to go to bed. You can do it tonight too! You are getting ready to quit this altogether."

- LISTEN TO YOUR CHILD: Thumbsucking can be a way your child shuts off communication with others. Therefore, listen with full attention to anything he says about it. Solutions for his feelings do not have to be found right then. Simply allow him the opportunity to speak.

- DON'T GET CAUGHT UP IN HIS EMOTION: The child may have a tantrum about some aspect of the program, but it will not help to argue about the rules, try to calm him, or remind him that he loves you. It may help to listen to him vent or to answer him with silence. Don't be afraid to send him to his room until he calms down. Afterward, listen to his grievance and offer love and direction, "I know that feels really bad. This is something that you will have to get control over." After the storm, make adjustments to the routine if appropriate.

- DESCRIBE THE CHILD'S CHANGING SELF-IMAGE: To get rid of thumbsucking is to discover a new self, one that was there all along but was hidden. Give positive words to describe your child's newly forming self-image, "You didn't like that huge dog, but you didn't suck your thumb. You are getting brave!"

- SHARE SIMILAR DIFFICULTIES YOU HAVE HAD: It may help gain your child's respect by telling him about how hard it was for you when you stopped a particular behavior, "Remember when I used to yell at you every time you left your bike in the driveway? I used to get so mad that it was easy to yell at you. But that was wrong. Do you remember that I told you I would never yell at you again and then I forgot a couple of times? Well, it was hard for me to stop, but I stopped. You can stop too."

• EXPRESS YOUR OWN FEELINGS: Be honest with your child about how the thumbsucking habit negatively affects you, "It's inappropriate for a child your age to suck the thumb at the grocery store. It makes me feel uncomfortable. I don't like it."

Praise the Child

Everyone loves to be praised and children are no exception. We love to hear how good we are and how well we've done. Let's face it, praise makes us feel good. Receiving praise for doing well in the process of eliminating a difficult thumbsucking habit gives a child the boost he needs to keep going. Remember, behaviors that are praised tend to show up more often.

• PRAISE THE CHILD DIRECTLY: Be specific, "Hey, you're not sucking your thumb right now. That's fabulous."

• PRAISE THE CHILD FOR DOING SOMETHING ELSE: When your child is doing something else that is noteworthy, praise him, "I like that castle you're making." This will keep your child's attention on that activity and he will continue it for a longer period of time.

• BRAG ABOUT THE CHILD: Let your child overhear you say something positive about his new behavior to someone else. For example, say to a friend, "We drove all the way to my folks' house, stayed the night, and drove all the way back the next day. David kept his hands out of his mouth the whole time. I am very proud of him."

- PRAISE THE CHILD FOR REMEMBERING THE PLAN: When your child suddenly remembers that he is on a new course, praise him for his good memory, "Whew! I'm glad you remembered to lotion your hands tonight. I almost forgot."

- PRAISE THE CHILD FOR NOT MAKING A FUSS: When your child looks like he wants to lose control but he holds his countenance, make sure to praise him, "Wow. You really wanted to scream about that, didn't you? But you didn't. That is very *good*. You are getting control over this thing."

- SUM UP THE CHILD'S ACCOMPLISHMENT: Use language that tells the child about their accomplishments in the area of thumbsucking. Say, "You started to suck your thumb and then you put your hand down. That's what I call determination."

- PRAISE DESCRIPTIVELY: Use words that convey your appreciation of the changing behavior. For example, as you take the child's hand, say, "I like to hold your hand now because you are keeping it dry!"

Use Disapproval

In today's society, we have developed the notion that it is inappropriate to use shame and disapproval when rearing a child. Well, if we do not disapprove of anything they do, then we are raising them to be wild and unaccountable to us or to anyone else. Shame and disapproval do not have to break the little spirit of a child, but shame and disapproval can be used to shape a child's behavior. Perhaps we could call this *healthy* shame and *healthy* disapproval.

- OCCASIONALLY EXPRESS STRONG DISAPPROVAL: It is appropriate on occasion to tell your child in strong words that you do not approve of thumbsucking. For example, "I will not have thumbsucking in this house! Thumbsucking is no good! Put your hands down!"

- DRAG OTHERS INTO IT: Don't be afraid to express how others will think of your child if he sucks his thumb, but do it sparingly, "You can't suck your thumb during baseball practice. What will the other boys think of you? They are going to think that you are scared or that you are a baby! You don't want them to think that! Keep your hands away from your mouth during baseball practice!"

Show Respect for the Child's Dilemma

Honor the fact that your child is trying to do a difficult thing: to stop a habit. Have you ever tried to stop a habit? How about overeating, smoking, drinking, or spending too much money? Any habit is hard to break. Show empathy by saying, "It's hard to remember not to suck your thumb sometimes."

Summary

Children should be given ample opportunity to express their feelings about the process of eliminating thumbsucking. Parents should answer a child's questions honestly and briefly, and should listen, mirror back the child's sentiments, encourage strength, and refrain from getting caught up in his emotion. Parents also should show respect for the child's dilemma and praise him for his efforts. Parents should not fear periodic use of healthy shame and disapproval but should limit use of these techniques.

Additional Information

The following information is a good supplement to the ideas and techniques presented in the previous chapters. This section contains information on:

1. Cribs and cages
2. Special needs
3. Behavior resources
4. Products

Weigh the Benefits of Cribs and Cages

Intraoral devices can be an effective solution for children who need to break a thumbsucking habit. These devices fit nicely into today's quick-fix-by-the-professional mentality. The placement of an intra-oral device, commonly called *cribs*, *cages*, *rakes*, *buttons*, and many other names, is the treatment method of choice by many orthodontists and parents. Each appliance looks like its name. Typically, one is placed on the teeth and/or on the roof of the mouth in such a way that the child's typical thumb-sucking position is blocked or hampered. For example, a rake is a device that looks like the head of a small rake, with long tines that hang down, or back, toward the tongue from behind the upper front teeth. In some cases, these long tines actually prevent the child from getting suction on the thumb.

Still, intraoral devices are considered by many to be a last resort because they have several drawbacks. Children sometimes find a way around an intraoral device by placing the thumb in the mouth in a different position. Thus, they can continue the thumb-sucking habit with the device in place. Also, even when a thumbsucking habit appears to be broken by using a device, once the appliance is removed, children can return to their habit quite easily. Intraoral devices also may prevent correct oral-rest posture, correct learning of selective speech sounds, and they can be painful to the tongue.

When an intraoral device fails, it is not the problem of the device nor the orthodontist who placed it. The real problem is in assuming that the device will work alone without any supporting activity to assure carryover once the appliance is removed. Many children need a complete thumbsucking-elimination program to make the transition, including ways to change, monitor their progress, and help them maintain new habits. An intraoral device is more effective as one component of a multifaceted thumbsucking-elimination program.

Special Needs

Special adaptations to the suggestions offered in this book may need to be made when a child has special mental or physical conditions. First, thumbsucking should be viewed in light of both the child's chronological age *and* developmental age. For example, thumbsucking might be allowed in a four-year-old child who functions more like a one-year-old child because thumbsucking would be appropriate for him developmentally.

Second, thumbsucking may be of benefit to a child with severe developmental disabilities regardless of age. For example, a severely impaired eight-year-old child who is tube fed may benefit from sucking the thumb because of the way it helps to strengthen and organize sucking movements. Other mouthing activities also should be included.

Third, the status of oral-tactile sensitivity should be considered when opting to eliminate a thumbsucking problem. For example, a child with oral-tactile hypersensitivity may be using thumbsucking to prevent oral movement or to neutralize unpleasant oral-tactile experiences. The thumb may help the child achieve a high guard position or a protective position with the tongue. The thumbsucking-elimination program should be initiated after steps have been taken to help the child normalize oral-tactile sensitivity. Once oral sensitivity begins to diminish, the need for thumbsucking may be eliminated, or at least it will be one step closer to elimination.

Fourth, the benefits of thumbsucking must be weighed in the balance against chronological age and social appropriateness. For example, a teenage child may like to engage in mouthing, and therapists may determine that mouthing is beneficial to the child's oral-motor development. However, the child's age and the fact that he is moving into larger social circles at school and in society may prohibit oral behaviors. Many of these children are unable to distinguish between when it is OK to put something into the mouth and when it is not. Mouthing behaviors, including thumbsucking, will have to be eliminated. A behavior modification plan will benefit him.

Speech-language pathologists, occupational therapists, physical therapists, and special education teachers involved with a child who has multiple disabling conditions should have input into a family's decision about eliminating a thumbsucking habit. Families should feel free to discuss thumbsucking during team meetings in which educational plans are being made for the child. Families need to keep in mind, however, that the professionals assigned to any one specific educational or medical team may or may not know much about eliminating a thumbsucking habit. If they don't, parents may need to take the lead on this issue by sharing ideas and information and guiding treatment plans.

Behavior Resources

Some parents may need to learn how to manage their child's general behavior before tackling the thumbsucking issue. Most local community colleges, public schools, and religious groups offer fairly inexpensive, or even free, parenting courses. Look for one that will teach child development and behavior management. Also, family counseling is an option and is available through private means or your local hospital, church, synagogue, or temple. Selected television and radio programs offer talk shows and lectures on child rearing: Christian AM talk radio offers a great selection of programs presented from biblical perspectives. Books and magazines also may be very useful for you in your attempts to learn better behavior management for your children. A few print resources are suggested here:

- *How to Talk So Kids Will Listen and How to Listen So Kids Will Talk*. This fabulous book by Adele Faber and Elaine Mazlish (Avon Books, 1980) contains practical advice on communicating with your children in ways that foster their development in all areas.

Although reading the entire book is recommended, you can read through the cartoons and learn a lot about this topic before ever reading the text itself. Read it from beginning to end, and keep it in the bathroom for quick reference.

- *The New Dare to Discipline*. This book and the audiotapes of Dr. James Dobson speaking on this topic will help set your mind straight about disciplining your child. If his biblical advice is taken, it will help you feel in control of otherwise uncontrollable situations at all levels of child-rearing. (Focus on the Family, Colorado Springs, CO: 1-800-232-6459.)
- *Good Behavior*. This resource by Stephen Garber, et al (Villard Books: NY, 1990), contains hundreds of practical behavior-management suggestions for children of all ages.
- *The Doctor Laura Show*: This nationally syndicated weekday AM radio broadcast will leave no doubt in your mind about who should be in charge of your kids—you! This call-in talk show is an excellent source of information about ethical child-rearing practices. Dr. Laura comes on quite strong—she says she "preaches, teaches, and nags." But after regular listening (three months or more) you will come to understand her perspective and her wisdom. She always puts children's needs first and her child-rearing advice is first class.

Products

Several companies offer toys, tools, rewards, motivational objects, and continuing education materials that are specifically designed to help parents and professionals with the elimination of thumbsucking and other oral habits.

OMT Materials
PO Box 66168, Sacramento, CA 95866-1688. Phone: 1-916-488-8833. OMT provides therapy and continuing education materials for problems with swallowing, thumbsucking, and related issues.

- STICKERS: Clever, colorful stickers related to the oral mechanism to use as motivators and rewards.
- ZICKEFOOSE LIP EXERCISER: A small device designed to exercise the lip muscles.
- ORAL MYOFUNCTIONAL THERAPY RUBBER STAMPS: Includes stamps of an elephant saying "Remember?" and other stamps that motivate and reward good mouth and lip behavior.
- THUMBBUDDIES: A specially designed soft glove for the thumb and index finger that is worn as a reminder not to suck. Designed with faces and hair, the thumb and index finger of the Thumbbuddies can talk to one another and give each other encouragement about eliminating thumbsucking. Practical and fun!

Speech Dynamics, Inc.
27349 Jefferson Ave., #205, Temecula, CA 92590. Phone: 1-800-337-9049. Speech Dynamics offers many therapy and continuing education materials designed to help therapists and parents with all kinds of oral-motor problems in children, including thumbsucking.

- MY THUMB AND I: A practical program that helps children to stop their digit-sucking habit in a positive, direct way. Presented in workbook fashion, this simple 10-step sequential remediation program helps children ages 6–10 gain self-control and self-confidence while eliminating the oral habit.

- T-GUARD: A clear plastic, nonabrasive device that fits loosely around the thumb, rendering it impossible for the child to get suction. It is designed in such a way that it cannot be removed until cut off with scissors. Therefore, it is much better and safer to use than other items that are taped.
- MOUTHING TOYS: An excellent collection of chewy mouthing objects appropriate for young children. Increases oral awareness and control in children whose thumbsucking problem is related to general oral-motor delay or disorder.
- TIME-TIMER: A clock-like device that literally shows the passage of time. Great for teaching young children about time. Use it to set time limits on sucking.

Zimco Products
1530 Bellevue Way SE, Suite B, Bellevue, WA 98004. Phone: 1-206-746-6929. Joe Zimmerman, SLP, and his wife, Diana, provide orofacial myofunctional therapy services to clients in the greater Seattle area. They sell a collection of thumbsucking gadgets that are fun additions to a thumbsucking-elimination program.

- GAUZETAPE: Self-sticking bandaging gauze that does not stick to the skin like adhesive, nor does it come off easily in water. Placed on the thumb, Gauzetape is a comfortable reminder not to suck.
- LIP COOKIE CUTTER: A lip-shaped cookie cutter that can be used to make cookies, biscuits, or Jell-o jigglers. A fun way to remind a child not to suck the thumb.

- ZIP-LIP PURSES: Handsome, lip-shaped, red vinyl purses ideal for lunch money or lipstick. Provides an inconspicuous reminder to keep the thumb out of the mouth and lips together.
- LIP PUNCH: A small metal paper punch that creates a lip shape cutout. It's fun to punch lip holes on papers or to glue the cutouts onto other items to help the child remember not to put the thumb in the mouth and to keep the lips together.
- LIPS KEY CHAIN: A key chain with a lips tag. Another subtle reminder. The lips key chain can be used for keys or to attach to backpacks.
- PRISM LIPS STICKERS: Lip stickers made of shiny red material that makes interesting visual patterns. Can be placed anywhere as a reminder.
- MOUTH PENCIL SHARPENER: Small pencil sharpener in the shape of lips. Can be a secret reminder at school to keep the thumb out of the mouth and to keep the lips together.
- VELVET LIP STICKERS: Tiny, velvety-soft lip stickers that can be placed in a notebook, on mirrors, in dresser drawers, on lunchboxes, or almost anywhere the child may need a subtle reminder not to suck.
- *THUMB AND FINGER SUCKING QUESTIONS AND ANSWERS*: Small, two-color pamphlet that addresses the dental problems associated with excessive thumbsucking and finger sucking habits. Sold in lots of fifty.
- THUMBSUCKING CHERUB FIGURINE: An 8.5-inch angel figurine that is sucking its thumb. A great reminder of how infantile it looks to suck the thumb. Comes in white porcelain and terra cotta.
- *ATLAS OF THE MOUTH*: This illustrated textbook presents the anatomy of the mouth as well

as its physiological and pathological conditions. Published by the American Dental Association.

Professional Resources

To help locate professionals in your area who may be able to help you plan and implement a thumbsucking-elimination plan, the following national and international associations are listed:

American Speech-Language-Hearing Association
10801 Rockville Pike
Rockville, MD 20852
Phone: 1-301-897-5700
www.asha.org

American Dental Association
211 E. Chicago Ave.
Chicago, IL 60611
Phone: 1-312-440-2500
www.ada.org

International Association of Orofacial Myology
PO Box 2143
Saratoga, CA 95070

How to Stop Thumbsucking $14.95
How to Stop Drooling $14.95

Pam Marshalla's How-to Series gives you easy-to-understand resources that help to reduce or eliminate your child's thumbsucking and excessive drooling. Includes practical guidelines, solutions, and activities for home or therapy.

Becoming Verbal with Childhood Apraxia $19.95
New Insights on Piaget for Today's Therapy

Particularly relevant for minimally verbal children who have been diagnosed with apraxia or dyspraxia of speech. Includes the organization and facilitation of early sound and word emergence.

Oral Motor Techniques in Articulation and Phonological Therapy $49.95

Includes all the basics of oral-motor therapy for improving jaw, lip, and tongue control, and for normalizing oral-tactile sensitivity. Written for both the professional and student speech-language pathologist, the text guides the reader through fundamental techniques used in treatment. An excellent supplemental text for courses on motor speech disorders, articulation, phonology, feeding, and dysphagia.

Successful R Therapy $49.95

Learn how to train the most difficult R clients. From the cornerstone R to conversational speech, this takes you through every stage of articulation therapy for the misarticulated R. Includes deep insights into the relationships between oral-motor skills, auditory processing and articulation control.

Order Today

1 Select titles

Title	Price	Quantity	Total
How to Stop Thumbsucking	$14.95		$
How to Stop Drooling	$14.95		$
Becoming Verbal with Developmental Apraxia	$19.95		$
Oral-Motor Techniques	$49.95		$
Successful R Therapy	$49.95		$

2 Find total

Wholesale prices available on request

U.S. shipping (1–4 books = $3.95; 5–10 books = $7.50)	$
International shipping (1–4 books = $9.95; 5–10 books = $14.95)	$
WA residents add 8.9% sales tax	$
Total	$

3 Mail order

Send check or money order to
Marshalla Speech and Language
11417 - 124th Ave NE, #202
Kirkland, WA 98033

Questions?
(425) 828-4361

www.pammarshalla.com

Name:_____

Street:_____

City:_____

State:_____ Zip: _____

Phone: (____)_____

E-mail:_____

MSL
Marshalla Speech and Language